"There will be a bake sale,"
said Miss Hume.
"You can bring cakes to sell."

1

Kate spoke with Mom at home.

"Can we make a cake?"

"I hope so," said Mom.

The Bake Sale

written by Lisa Shulman
illustrated by Rick Brown

SAXON
PUBLISHERS

THIS BOOK IS THE PROPERTY OF:

STATE_____	Book No. _____
PROVINCE_____	Enter information
COUNTY_____	in spaces
PARISH_____	to the left as
SCHOOL DISTRICT_____	instructed
OTHER_____	

ISSUED TO	Year Used	CONDITION	
		ISSUED	RETURNED

**PUPILS to whom this textbook is issued must not write on any page
or mark any part of it in any way, consumable textbooks excepted.**

1. Teachers should see that the pupil's name is clearly written in ink in the spaces above in
   every book issued.
2. The following terms should be used in recording the condition of the book: New; Good; Fair;
   Poor; Bad.

Mom said, "Use those eggs."

Kate broke one egg.

Then Kate broke two more.

Kate tore a hole in a bag.

Kate broke a plate.

What a big mess Kate made!

Mom put the cake in to bake.
The cake got hot.

Dad came in.

"I smell smoke," he said.

"Is the cake done?"

Kate ate some cake.

"I will name this Stone Cake,"
said Kate.

"I cannot take this to the sale."

Kate got a cake from the store.

Blake's cake is the same
as Kate's.

"Twin cakes!" said Miss Hume.

The End

Understanding the Story

Questions are to be read aloud by a teacher or parent.

1. Why does Kate want to make a cake?

2. Why does she call her cake Stone Cake?

3. What does Kate bring to the bake sale?

4. Who brings in a cake just like Kate's?

Saxon Publishers, Inc.
Editorial: Barbara Place, Julie Webster, Grey Allman, Elisha Mayer
Production: Angela Johnson, Carrie Brown, Cristi Henderson
Brown Publishing Network, Inc.
Editorial: Marie Brown, Gale Clifford, Maryann Dobeck
Art/Design: Trelawney Goodell, Camille Venti, Jillian Gordon
Production: Joseph Hinckley

Published by Harcourt Achieve Inc.

Saxon is a trademark of Harcourt Achieve Inc.

Printed in the United States of America
ISBN: 1-56577-975-4

2 3 4 5 6 7 8 446 12 11 10 09 08 07 06 05

Phonetic Concepts Practiced

a-consonant-e (bake)
o-consonant-e (home)
u-consonant-e (use)

Nondecodable Sight Words Introduced

done
one
two

ISBN 1-56577-975-4

9 781565 779754

Grade 1, Decodable Reader 13
First used in Lesson 42